# This Journal Belongs to

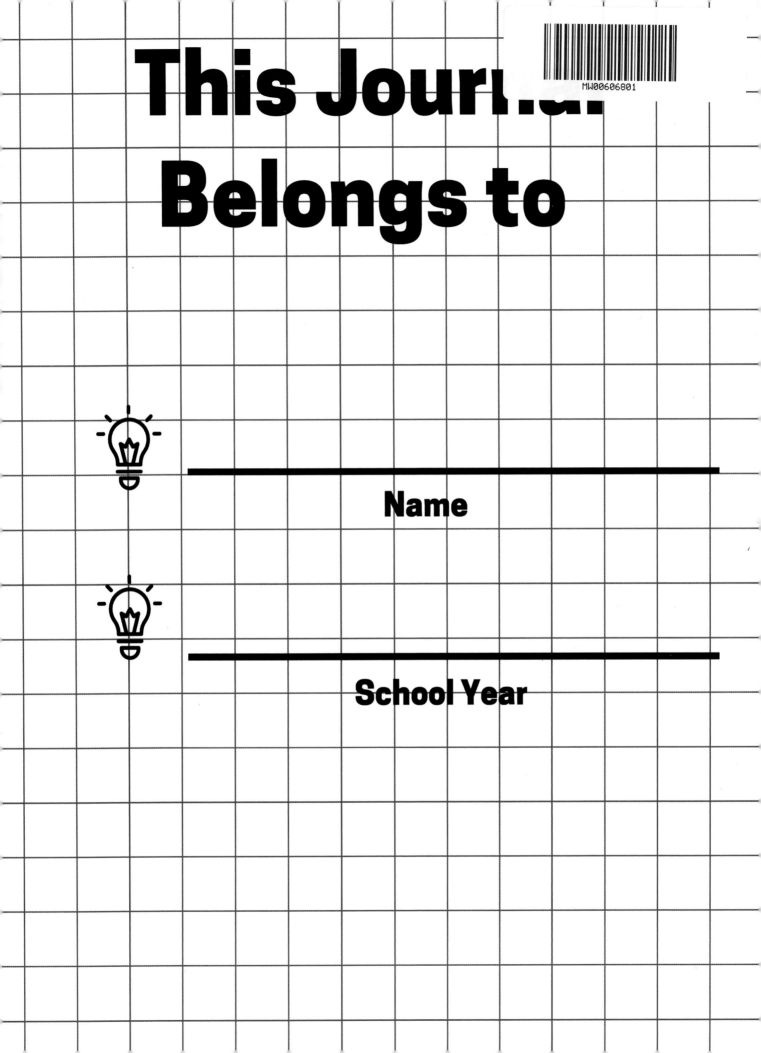

_____

**Name**

_____

**School Year**

# My School

**Name of School**

**Grade**

# All about

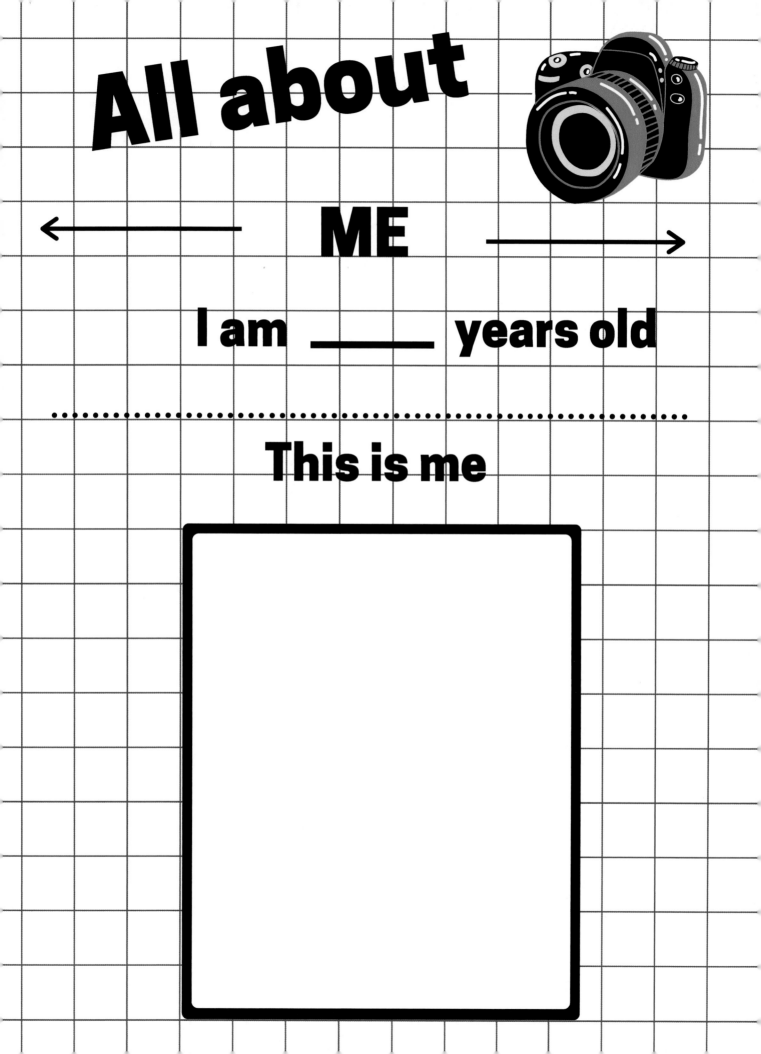

## ME

← —— —— ——

I am _____ years old

····················································

## This is me

# All about

## ME

Date of Birth _____

Height _____

# All about ME

# All about ME

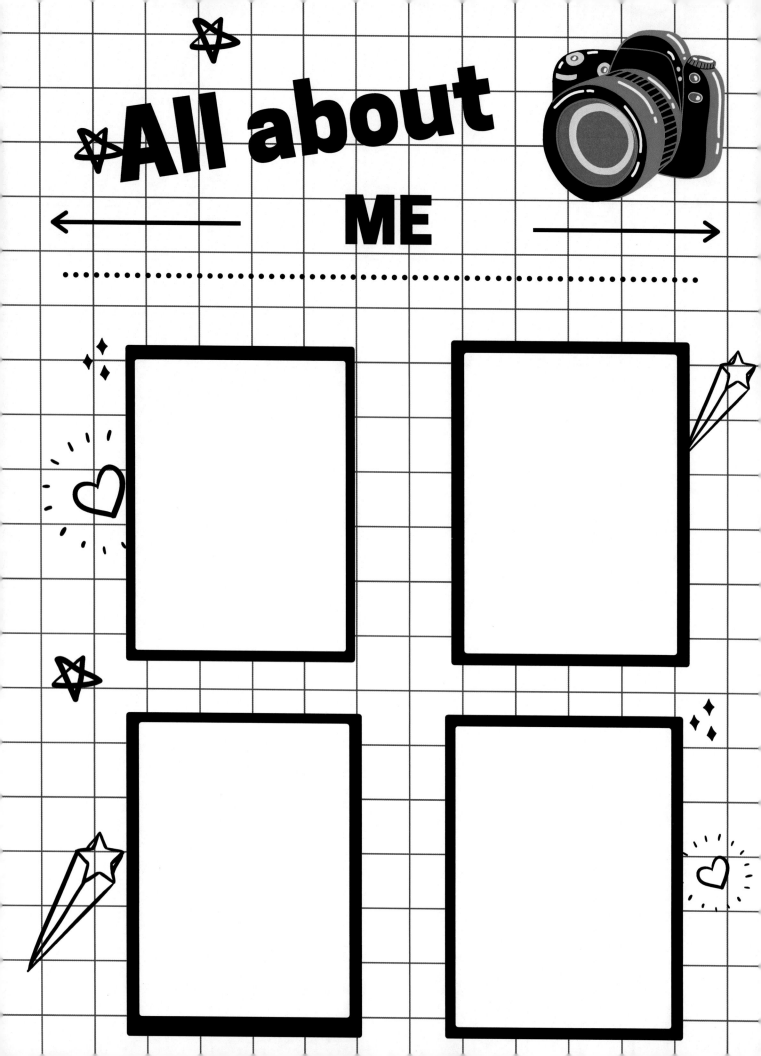

# All about
## MY FAMILY

# All about

## MY FAMILY

# MY FAVORITE OUTFIT

# MY FAVORITE SHOES

# MY FAVORITE HAIR STYLE

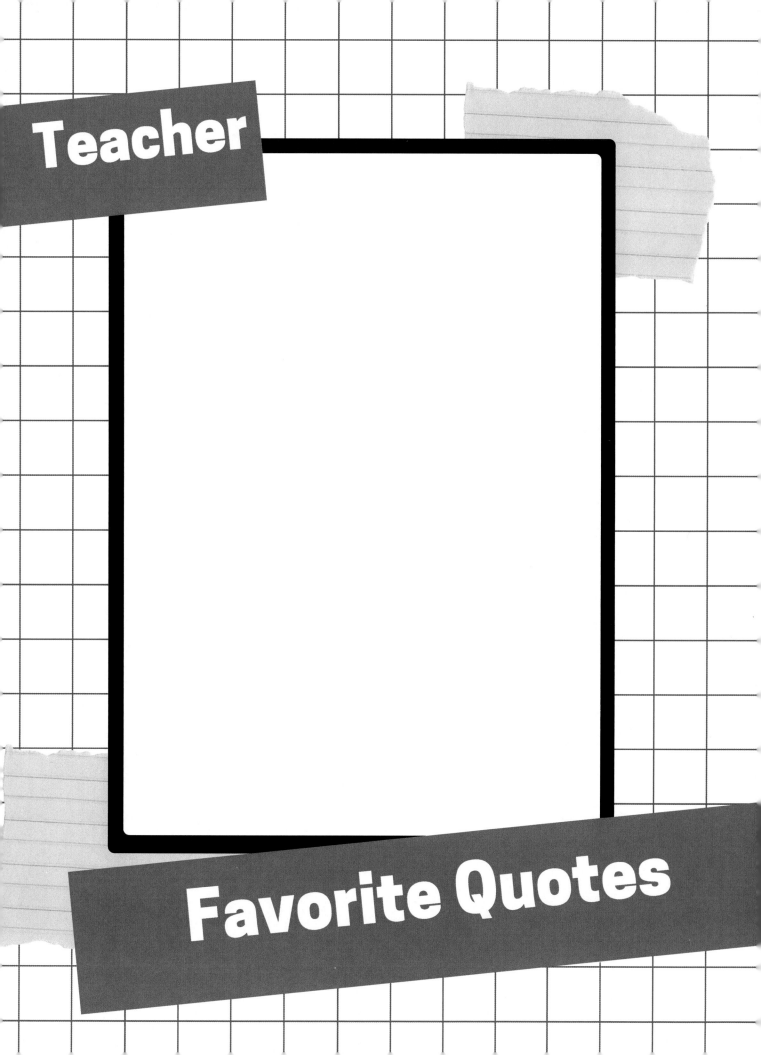

**Teacher**

**Favorite Quotes**

Favorite Quotes

School

Friends

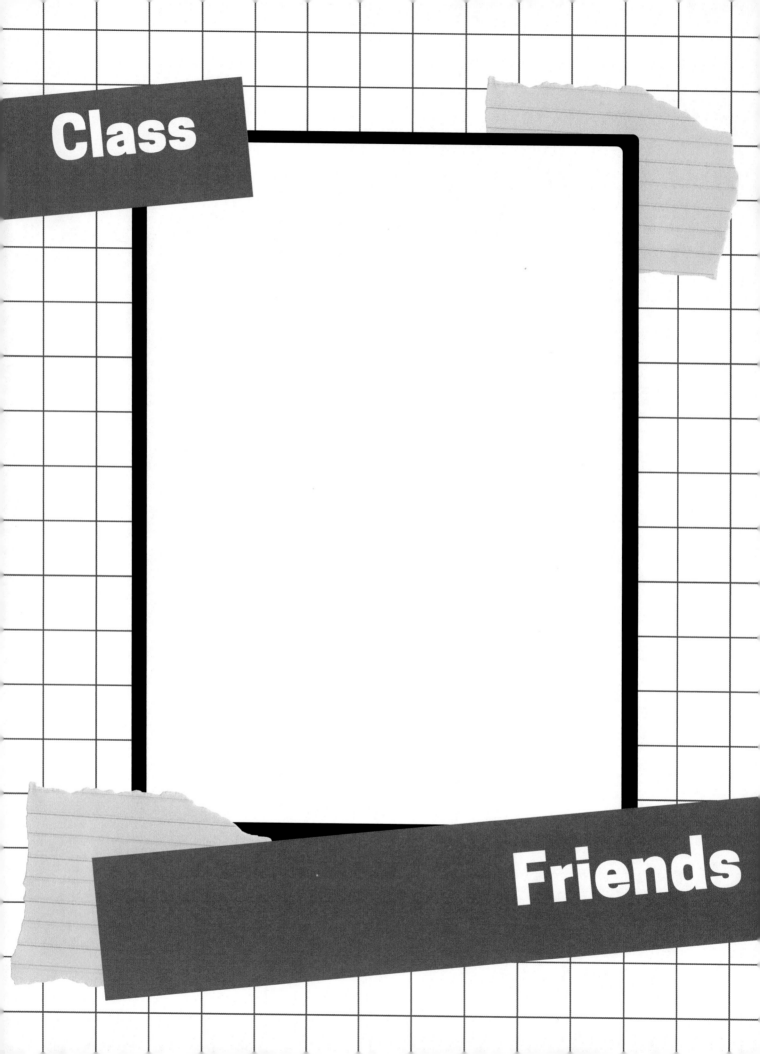

**Class**

**Friends**

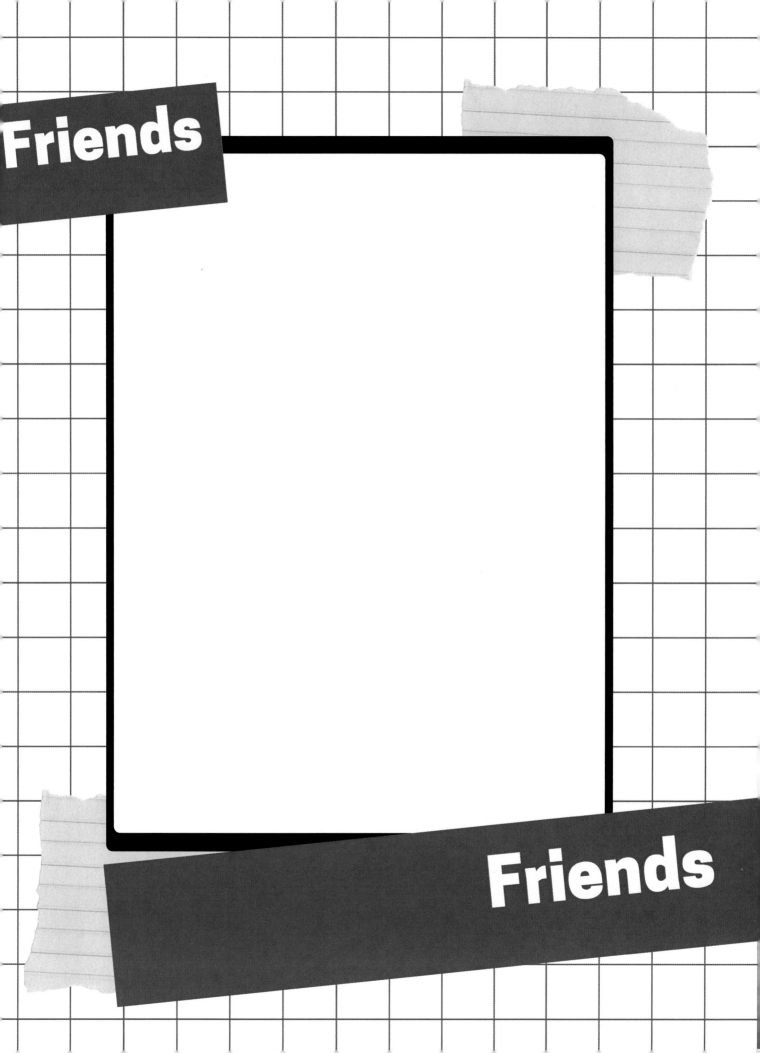

# FAVORITE DRINKS, FOOD, AND SNACKS

# SCHEDULE OF CLASSES

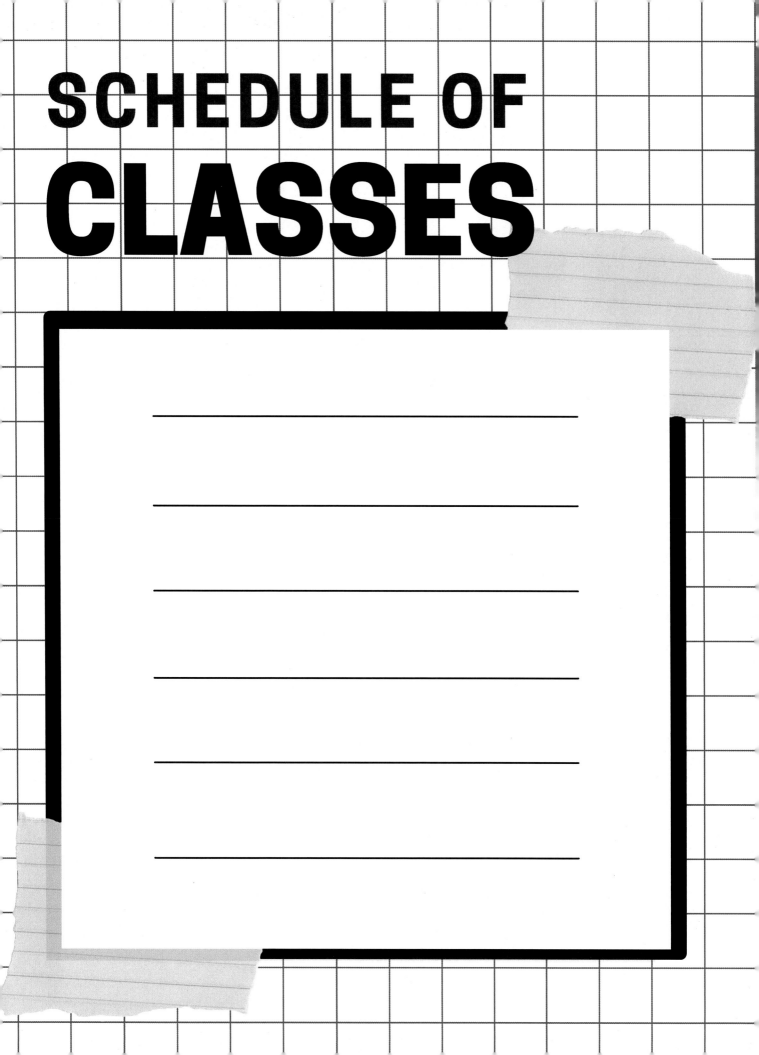

# CLASSROOM RULES

---

---

---

---

---

---

# MEMORIES

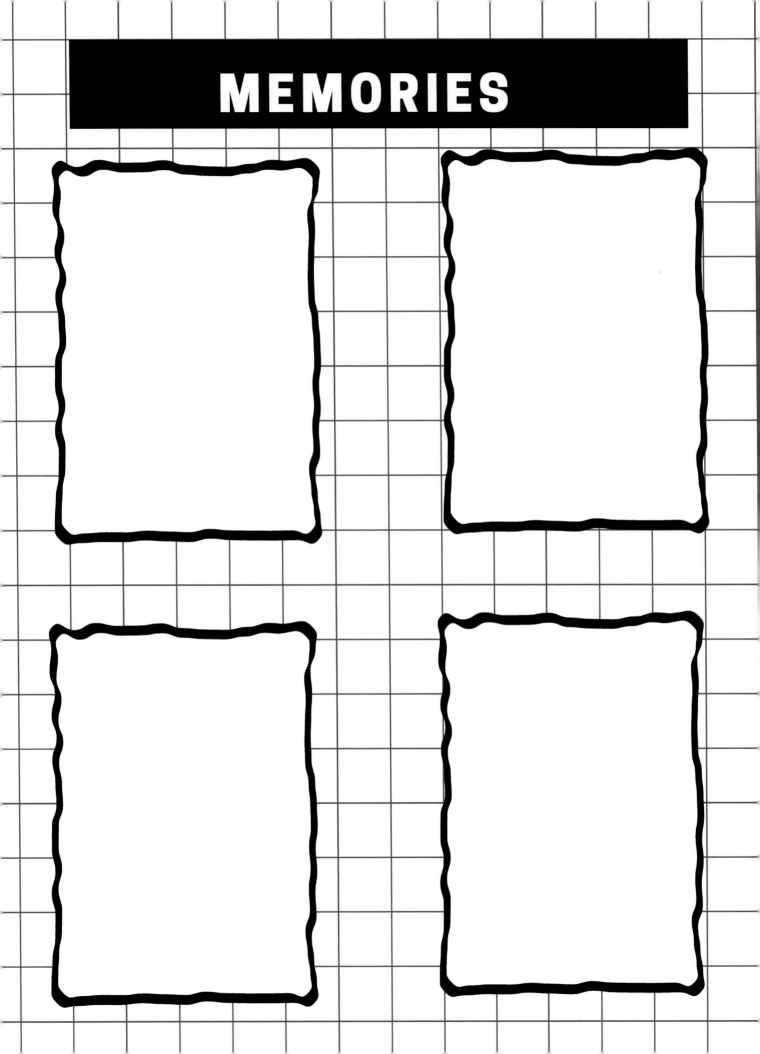

# MEMORIES

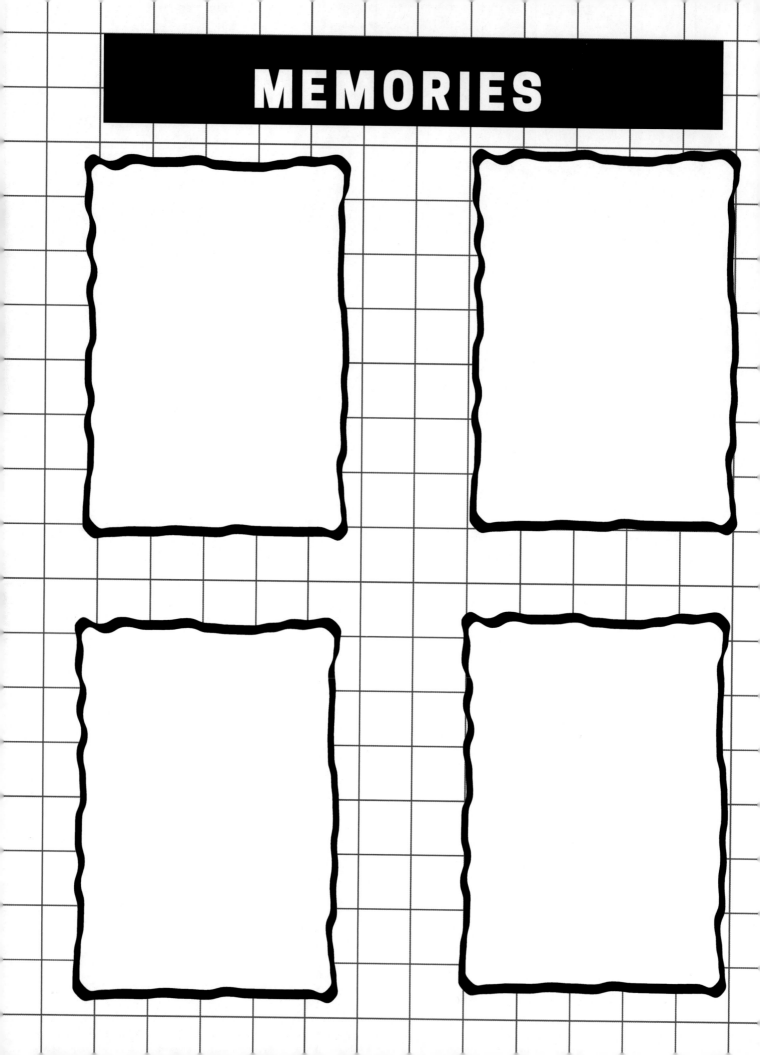

# INSPIRATIONS

# INSPIRATIONS

# ACTIVITIES

_____

_____

_____

_____

_____

_____

_____

# ACTIVITIES

# Favorite Movies

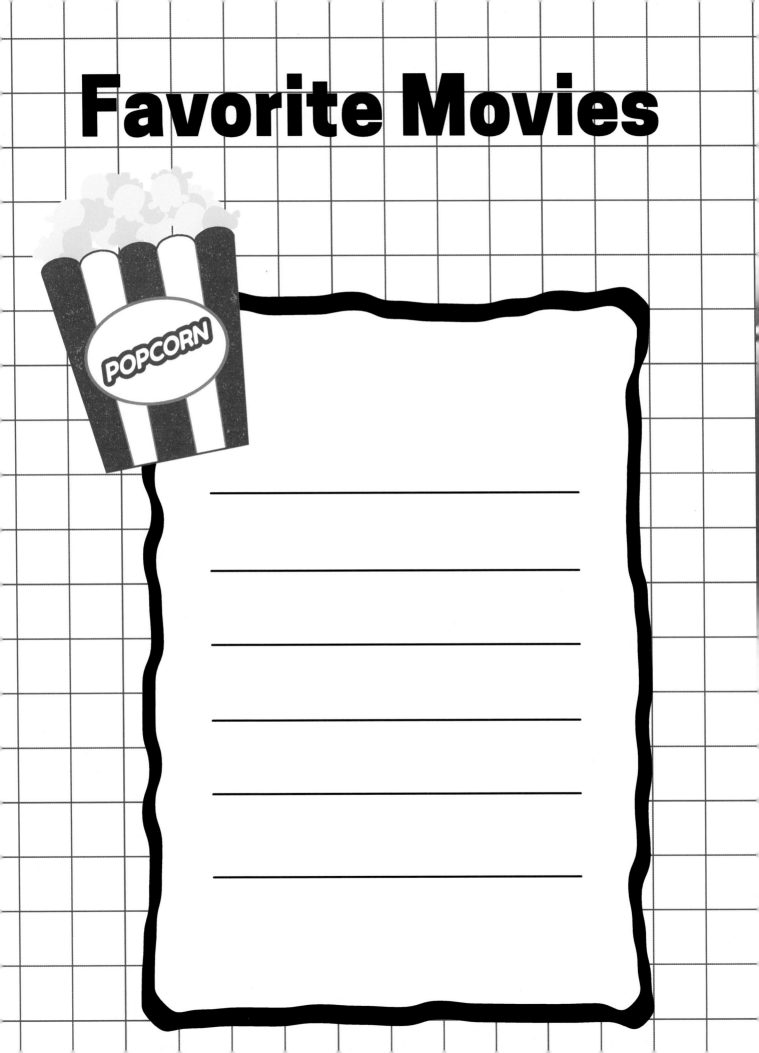

# Favorite Celebrities

# Favorite Songs

# FAVORITE BOOKS

_____

_____

_____

_____

_____

_____

_____

_____

# WHAT HAPPENED THIS YEAR

_____

_____

_____

_____

_____

_____

_____

_____

_____

_____

_____

# WHAT HAPPENED THIS YEAR

# PLANS FOR THE FUTURE

_____

_____

_____

_____

_____

_____

_____

_____

_____

_____

_____

# PUBLICATIONS

Treasures from the King
Finding Your Me
A Child's Tenth
When I Grow (Blow) Up
Shaping My Path
Toilet treats
Writing Your Story
The 52 Experience
Pen It, Volume I
Recipe Reminder
Pen It, Volume II
My Affirmation Journey
My School Year Journal
My Elementary School Year Journal
My Middle School Year Journal

1 Vision Empowerment Publishing
www.1visionempowerment.com
Artwork: Canva.com
Printed and Manufactured in the United States of America

FIRST PRINTING: April 2022
ISBN: 978-1-735607771

65720700R10020